Tom Thumb

Written by Gill Budgell

Illustrated by Steve Brown

Tom

fit

hid

fell

bed

Talk about the story

Ask your child these questions:

1 What size is Tom?

2 Where did Tom hide?

3 How do you think Tom felt when he was falling?

4 What did Tom fall on to?

5 Have you got any tiny toys?

6 Would you like to be tiny like Tom? Why/Why not?

Can your child retell the story using their own words?